Though amazing discoveries and fascinating achievements mark the 25th century, some things have not changed. Life itself may be far different, but death remains the same. Man's mortality cannot be denied and his desire to postpone his end still remains an unfulfilled quest.

But not for James T. Kirk, Captain of the Starship *Enterprise*. Forced down to a strange planet by an omnipotent cloud-like creature, Kirk is offered the incredible gift of immortality.

Surely he will gratefully embrace such an opportunity. But, no! Kirk soon finds out that the price he is expected to pay in return for everlasting life is far too dear. For him, there is something more precious than eternal life. So precious in fact, that he'd rather risk death than submit to such a...

METAMORPHOSIS

G000166037

OTHER **STAR TREK FOTONOVELS**™
YOU WILL ENJOY—

THE CITY ON THE
EDGE OF FOREVER

WHERE NO MAN
HAS GONE BEFORE

THE TROUBLE
WITH TRIBBLES

A TASTE
OF ARMAGEDDON

STAR TREK ™*

METAMORPHOSIS

written by **GENE L. COON**

adapted from the television series
created by **GENE RODDENBERRY**

RLI: $\dfrac{\text{VLM 6 (VLR 5–7)}}{\text{IL 5+}}$

METAMORPHOSIS
A Bantam Book / February 1978

ISBN 0-553-11349-6

Published simultaneously in the United States and Canada

---

*Bantam Books are published by Bantam Books, Inc. Its trade-
mark, consisting of the words "Bantam Books" and the por-
trayal of a bantam, is registered in the United States Patent
Office and in other countries. Marca Registrada. Bantam
Books, Inc., 666 Fifth Avenue, New York, New York 10019.*

PRINTED IN THE UNITED STATES OF AMERICA
0 9 8 7 6 5 4 3 2 1

CAST LIST

James T. Kirk, Captain
William Shatner

A man in his mid-30's whose strong independent nature and sympathetic soul make him a natural leader. His overriding concern is always the safety and well-being of his ship and its crew.

Mr. Spock, First Officer
Leonard Nimoy

Of Vulcan and Terran heritage, which accounts for his highly analytical mind and extraordinary strength. His life is ruled by reason and logic.

Leonard McCoy, M.D., Lt. Commander
DeForest Kelley

Senior Ship's Surgeon. Though surrounded by the most advanced equipment the 25th century can offer, he still practices medicine more with his heart than his mind.

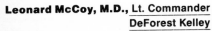

Zefram Cochrane
Glenn Corbett

Once famous throughout the galaxy, now doomed to an eternal life of loneliness.

Nancy Hedford
Elinor Donahue

She fears death only because she has never known life or love.

Sulu
Chief Helmsman
George Takei

Uhura, Lieutenant
Communications Officer
Nichelle Nichols

Montgomery Scott
Lt. Commander
James Doohan

INTERVIEW WITH ELINOR DONAHUE

by Caryl Eagle

Elinor Donahue, who appears as Nancy Hedford in this episode, is probably best known for her role as Betty in the Father Knows Best *series. Since the two roles differ so dramatically, I asked her how she got the part.*

E.D. The Line Producer called me and explained the character. I was interested and read the script. I decided to do it because it was such a radical change from my usual image. Although I was about thirty at the time, this was the first real woman I had to play. I'd like to have an opportunity to play the character again now that I'm older. The opening scenes where she was tough and liberated were very hard for me. But I learned a valuable lesson. The cinematographer, Jerry Finnerman, taught me that I didn't have to use big childlike expressions and motions to get the point across. I could do it with my voice and eyes...do it from inside. His suggestions have stood me in good stead and I'm very grateful.

C.E. Sounds like you got quite a bit out of the show.

E.D. I did, but I must admit that it also took quite a bit out of me. I was so anxious to do a good job that I must have lost ten pounds. When it came time for me to play the beautiful Companion-Person, the front of my costume had "droopitis." They finally had to take the scarf off of my head and put it around my shoulders to cover my chest. They were really *very* thoughtful!

C.E. Then you enjoyed working on the set?

E.D. Yes, it was lovely, very warm and comfortable. The prop man would fix lunch for us on a barbeque. The members of the regular cast were fine professional actors and wonderful people. Bill Shatner had the funniest sense of humor, Leonard Nimoy was a very kind man and DeForest Kelley was just a sweetheart.

C.E. Then everything went very smoothly?

E.D. Not quite everything. There was one problem, I remember. We had shot several scenes, including the shuttlecraft's landing, on the largest set at Paramount. They had to use a large crane for the long shots and a huge cyclorama of the galaxy. They were very difficult shots from a technical point of view. Well, somehow all that film got ruined and we had to reshoot all the scenes again. But I guess it all turned out O.K. because it certainly looks good in your Fotonovel.

METAMORPHOSIS

SPACE:

THE FINAL FRONTIER

THESE ARE THE VOYAGES OF
THE STARSHIP "ENTERPRISE."
ITS FIVE YEAR MISSION: TO
EXPLORE STRANGE NEW WORLDS
...TO SEEK OUT NEW LIFE AND
NEW CIVILIZATIONS...TO
BOLDLY GO WHERE NO MAN HAS
GONE BEFORE.

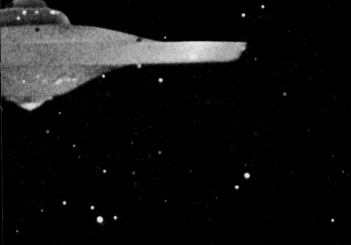

SHIP'S LOG:

STARDATE 3219.4

LT. COMMANDER SCOTT REPORTING IN THE
ABSENCE OF CAPTAIN KIRK. A SHUTTLE-
CRAFT BEARING THE CAPTAIN, FIRST
OFFICER SPOCK, AND CHIEF SURGEON
MCCOY HAS BEEN SENT TO EPSILON
CANARIS 3. THERE THEY ARE TO PICK UP
ASSISTANT FEDERATION COMMISSIONER
NANCY HEDFORD AND BRING HER BACK TO
THE "ENTERPRISE" FOR EMERGENCY
MEDICAL CARE.

WE ARE DUE TO RENDEZVOUS
WITH THE SHUTTLECRAFT IN EXACTLY
FOUR HOURS 29 MINUTES.

*On board
the shuttlecraft....*

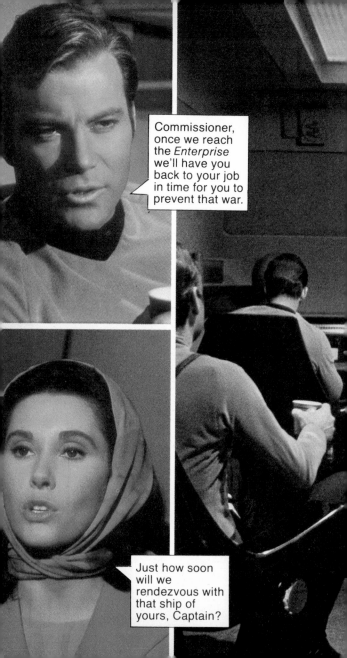

Helpless in the immensity of space, the shuttlecraft is pulled closer and closer to the powerful force.

Tossed like a toy boat in a swirling sea, the vessel is pitched back and forth by the unknown power.

Whatever it is, we've got it.

No, **it's** got **us.** Check the controls, Spock.

Helm is not answering, Captain. Neither do the pods.

Powerless to resist, the shuttlecraft is **totally enveloped** by the cloud-like force and is pulled at tremendous speeds closer and closer to Gamma Canaris N, while its passengers prepare themselves for the **inevitable crash.**

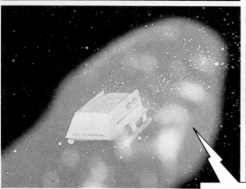

Brace yourselves! Grab on to something!

But **seconds** before they are about to hit, as if some great hand has reached out into space and has caught them in its protective grasp, their speed is suddenly checked and the craft floats slowly down to the surface where it nestles safely against a huge mountain.

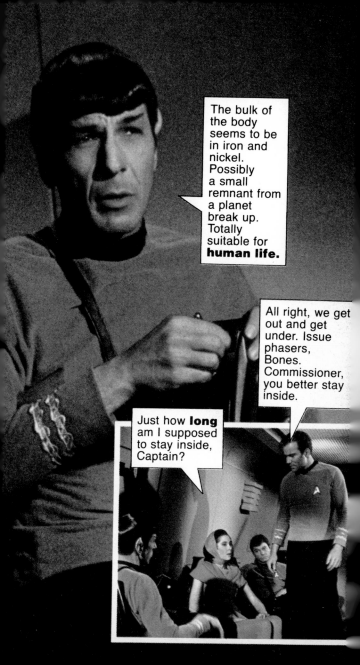

Slowly, carefully, McCoy begins to explore their new surroundings, each step taken **very gingerly.**

Ma'am, you'll excuse me for staring. But it's like food to a starving man!
Well, now that the **formalities** are completed...
NCC-1
U.S.S. ENTER
Hey, that's a nice ship. Simple and clean. Mind if I take a look?
Be our guest.

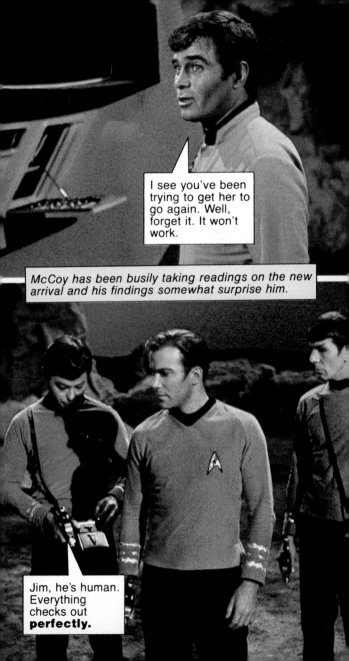

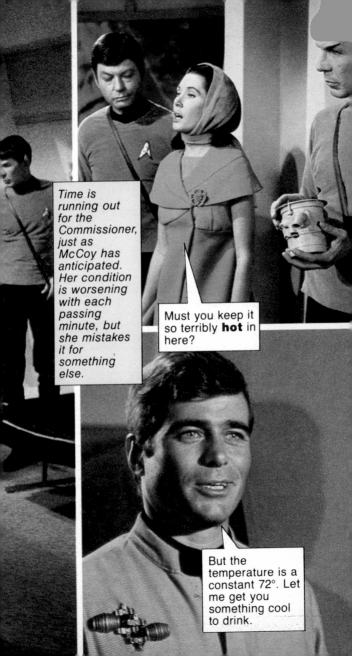

Time is running out for the Commissioner, just as McCoy has anticipated. Her condition is worsening with each passing minute, but she mistakes it for something else.

Must you keep it so terribly **hot** in here?

But the temperature is a constant 72°. Let me get you something cool to drink.

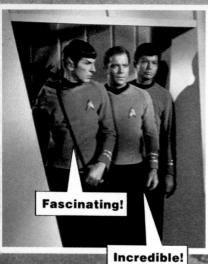

Fascinating!

Incredible!

A short distance away a huge swirling light dances above the ground...

...then quickly **vanishes.**
What was **that?**
I don't know, but I have a hunch our host does.

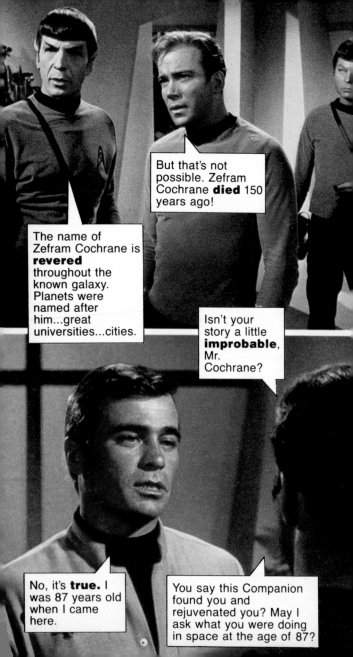

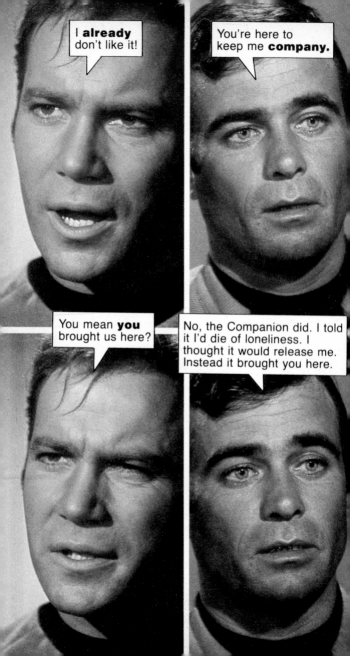

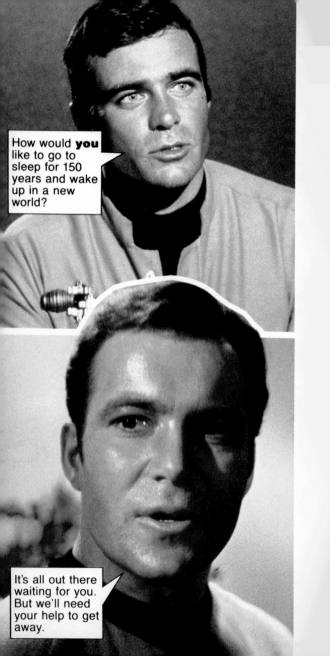

Following the Captain's orders, Spock has returned to the disabled shuttlecraft to check the power systems. Suddenly, a few feet away, the Companion materializes.

So total is Spock's concentration that he is unaware of its presence. However...

What a strange sensation. I feel as if someone...

...seems to **infuriate** the Companion to such a degree that it responds instantly with a blinding flash and a violent explosion that overpowers Spock and...

...**blasts** the shuttlecraft.

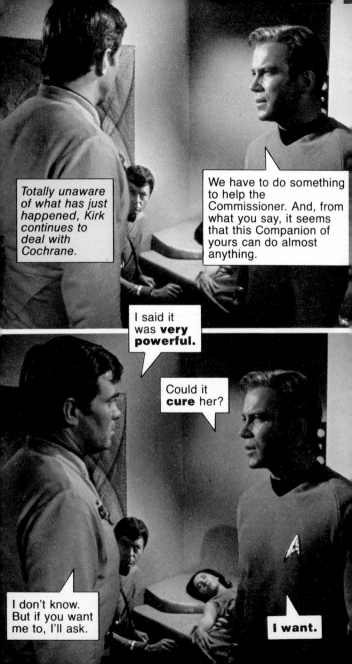

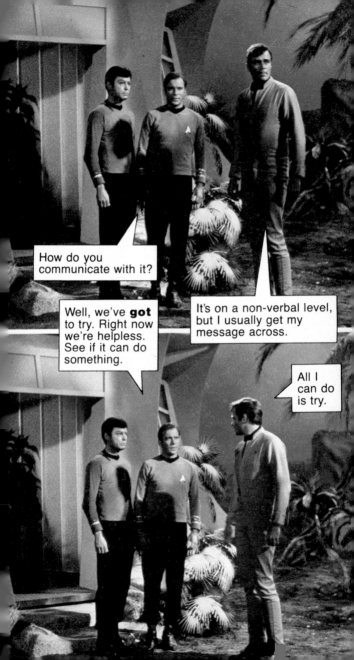

Cochrane moves out into the clearing and waits. His eyes closed...his body rigid. He waits.

Suddenly, the swirling light-form appears, engulfing him into its midst.

Mesmerized and fascinated the two men watch.

Bones, what do you make of **that?**

Almost a **symbiosis** of some kind. A sort of a joining.

When Spock fails to return to Cochrane's house, McCoy is sent back to the shuttlecraft to find him.
Hey, Spock- You in there?
I'm over here!
Following Spock's voice, McCoy finds him on the ground, slightly dazed.
Spock! Are you all right?
Yes, I'm fine, Doctor. But the Companion imparted to me a rather quaint old-fashioned **electrical shock.**

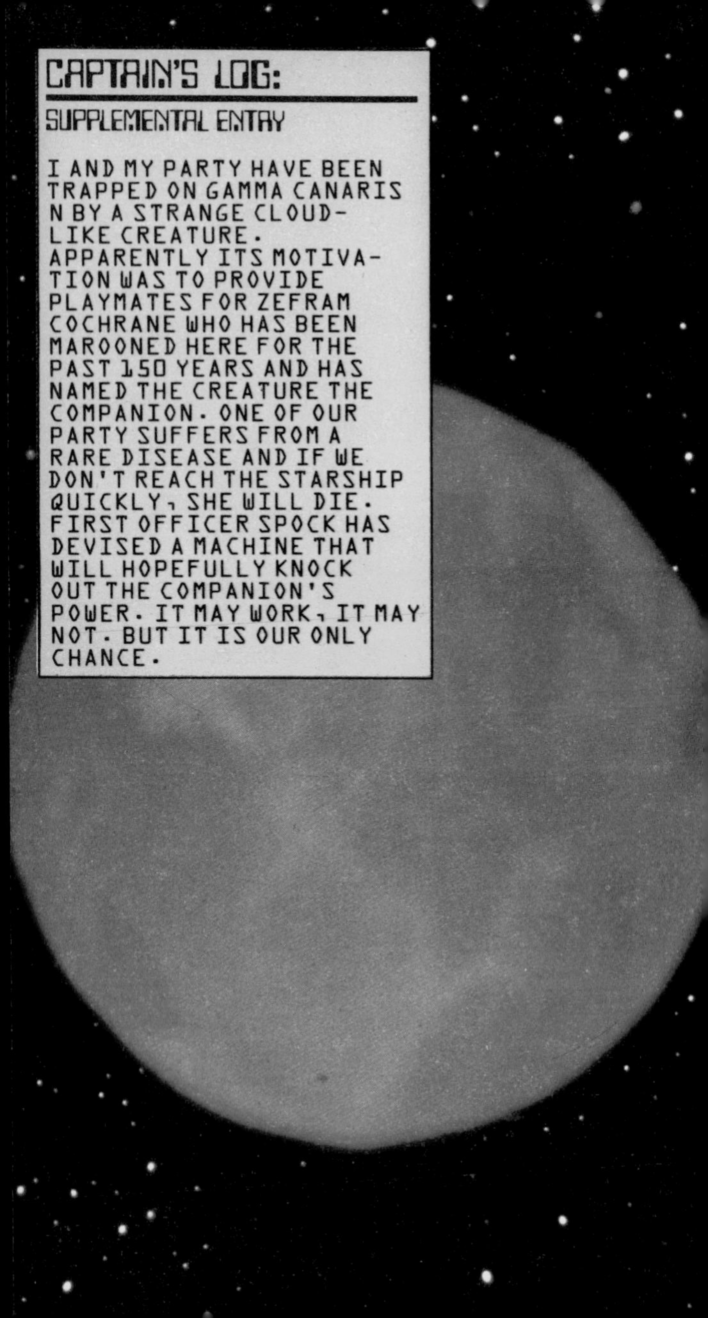

CAPTAIN'S LOG:

SUPPLEMENTAL ENTRY

I AND MY PARTY HAVE BEEN
TRAPPED ON GAMMA CANARIS
N BY A STRANGE CLOUD-
LIKE CREATURE.
APPARENTLY ITS MOTIVA-
TION WAS TO PROVIDE
PLAYMATES FOR ZEFRAM
COCHRANE WHO HAS BEEN
MAROONED HERE FOR THE
PAST 150 YEARS AND HAS
NAMED THE CREATURE THE
COMPANION. ONE OF OUR
PARTY SUFFERS FROM A
RARE DISEASE AND IF WE
DON'T REACH THE STARSHIP
QUICKLY, SHE WILL DIE.
FIRST OFFICER SPOCK HAS
DEVISED A MACHINE THAT
WILL HOPEFULLY KNOCK
OUT THE COMPANION'S
POWER. IT MAY WORK, IT MAY
NOT. BUT IT IS OUR ONLY
CHANCE.

As soon as Cochrane steps outside, Spock cautions the Captain.

You do realize that there is some risk. We do not know the extent of its powers.

Nor it **ours.**

Just as before, Cochrane waits, and in seconds the Companion joins him. As soon as Cochrane is enveloped by the creature...

Spock activates
the mechanism....

...throwing a
**tremendous
surge** of energy
directly into the
Companion. But
there is little
effect on the
creature.

Instantaneously, it rushes toward the house and turns its incredible powers directly on Kirk and Spock, striking them over and over again trying to choke the **very life** out of those who sought to hurt it.

Alerted by the cries, McCoy rushes into the room.

Stop it!! You're killing them! **Stop it!!**

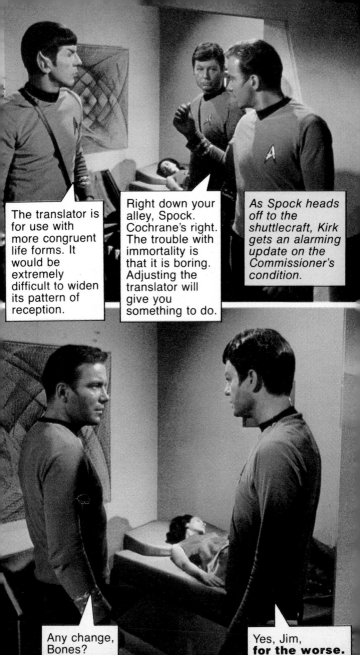

Companion, we wish to talk to you.

Indeed an understatement!

How can we communicate? Can you hear my thought? This is **most interesting.**

Not only does the translator perform as planned, but it also picks up a surprising signal.

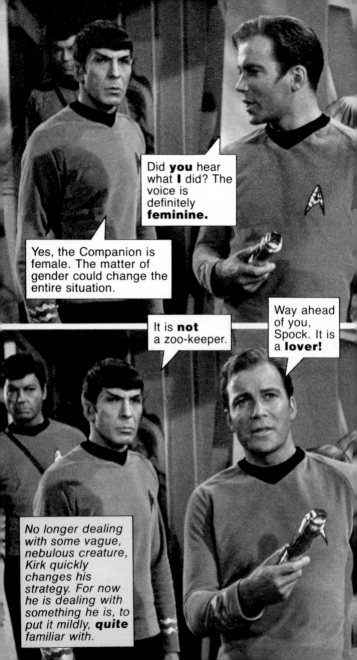

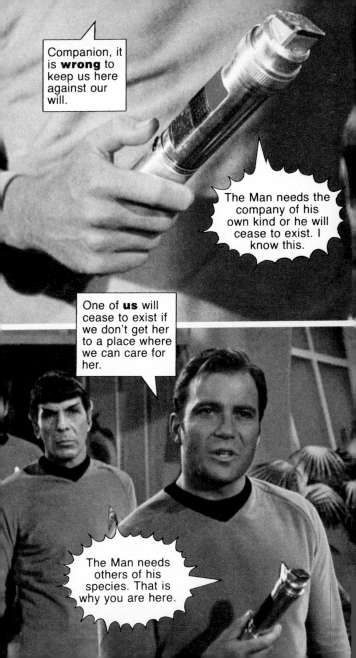

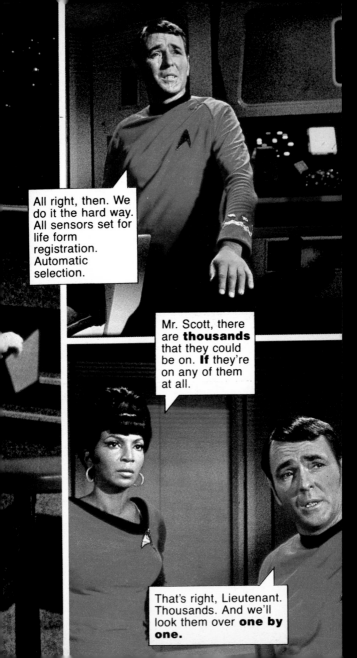

Meanwhile, on the planet, Kirk has decided to try a new strategy.
Companion, I must ask you something. Do you love the Man?
I do not understand.
Is he important to you? More important than **anything?** Is he as though he were a part of you?
He **is** part of me.

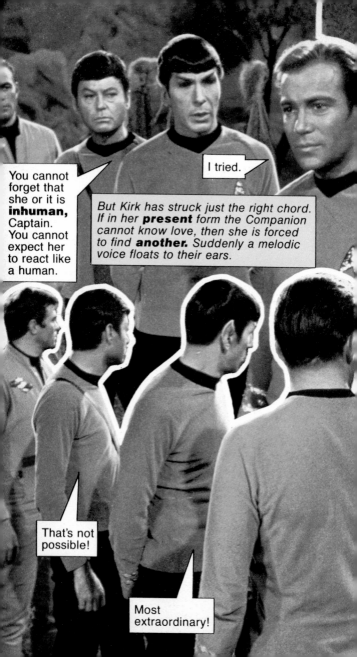

What are you talking about? Of course it's the Commissioner. Who **else** would it be?

No! It's the **Companion!**

Then you are both here in one body?

Yes. **We are one.**

But her interest does not lie with Spock. There is only **one person** she wishes to talk to. As she approaches Zefram he instinctively moves back, his body taut with tension.

We **frighten** you, Zefram. Why? We've never frightened you before.

We could do
nothing now to
stop you. The
Captain said we
would not know
love because we
were not human
and he was
right. But now
we are and we
will know all
things as
humans know
them. We will
know the change
of days and we
will know death.

But for the chance to
touch the hand of
Man...**nothing** is as
important.

And so the two who have been so close for so long join hands....

Go ahead, Cochrane. We have a few things to do.

...and take their first walk together, surrounded by the solitude of the landscape and the intimacy of the sound of silence.

To find love, here...**incredible**...but wonderful...**absolutely wonderful!**

For how could Kirk *know* how it will end? The lovers are just discovering that themselves.

There's a thousand planets out there...a thousand races. And just as soon as I learn my way around again, I'll show you everything. I want you to be happy, **very happy.**

But these words **erase** all traces of happiness from Nancy's face.

I **can't** go with you, Zefram.

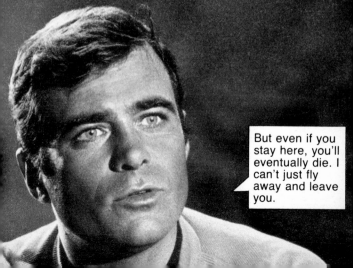

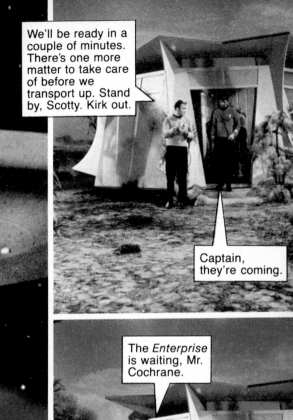

We'll be ready in a couple of minutes. There's one more matter to take care of before we transport up. Stand by, Scotty. Kirk out.

Captain, they're coming.

The *Enterprise* is waiting, Mr. Cochrane.

I'm not going, Captain. I **can't** take Nancy away from here. If I do, she'll **die.**

Think it over, Mr. Cochrane. There's a whole galaxy out there waiting to honor you.

I have honors enough.

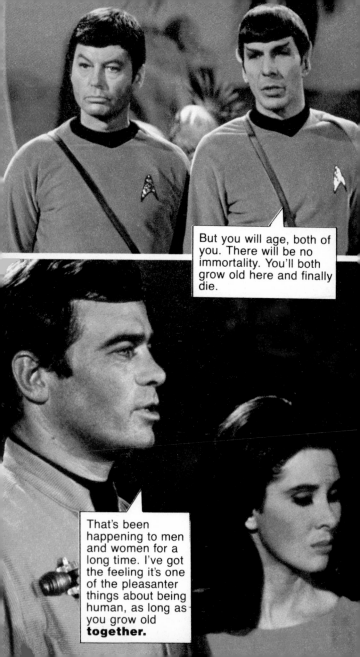

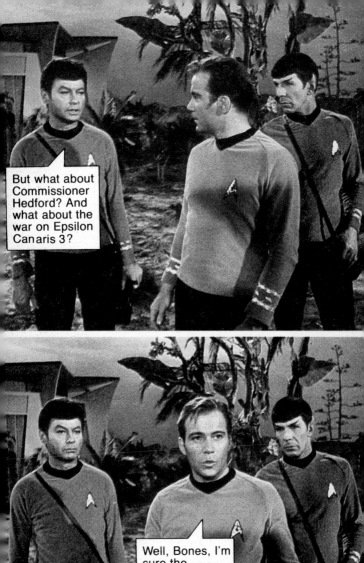

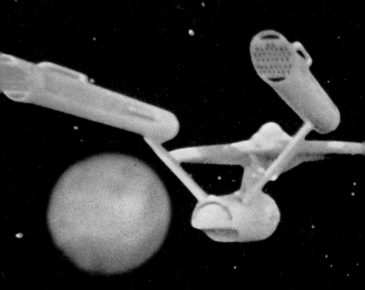

**THE
END**

GLOSSARY

Communicator—Portable device used primarily for maintaining voice contact between landing parties on a planet's surface and an orbiting spaceship.

Epsilon Canaris 3—An inhabited planet where the Federation has sent Commissioner Hedford hoping to prevent a potential war situation.

Gamma Canaris N—A small planetoid, whose atmosphere and gravity is identical to Earth's. It is probably the remains of the breakup of a larger planet.

Phasers—Personal weapons with adjustable settings ranging from "stun" to "kill."

Sakuro's Disease—A rare illness that left without the proper treatment, brings on a high fever followed by dropping blood pressure then delirium and finally death.

Ship's Log—Record keeping method of all activities on board the Starship. Entries are made by the Captain, or, in his absence, the officer in charge.

Shuttlecraft—A seven passenger ship used primarily for intra solar system missions.

Sickbay—The area of the Starship where all major medical procedures are performed.

Space Warp—The shifting of space resulting in changes and interphases of time, allowing people and matter to move into the past and future.

Stardate—Method of calculating time.

Transporter—Used to move crew and/or cargo from the Starship to planets and back by changing the object's molecular structure into energy which is beamed to a predetermined point where the original molecular formation is reconstructed.

Tricorder—Portable miniaturized computer capable of recording, analyzing and identifying all matter.

United Federation Of Planets—Democratic alliance of planets comprising several solar systems including Sol.

U.S.S. *Enterprise*—One of thirteen starships with a crew of approximately 430. Its eleven decks contain a completely self-supporting mini-city.

Universal Translator—Computer device capable of deciphering almost every language pattern in the universe by comparing the frequency of brain patterns, selecting those ideas and concepts it recognizes and providing the necessary grammar which it then translates into English.

Vulcan—Inhabitant of the planet Vulcan, identifiable by pointed ears, upswept eyebrows and sallow complexion. Vulcans' highly developed intelligence and logical minds rule out emotional responses.

Warp Drive—Method of propulsion exceeding the speed of light, achieved through the use of integrated matter and anti-matter.

STAR TREK QUIZ #5

In each question circle the one answer that best completes the sentence.

1. **A symptom of Sakuro's disease is:**
   a. loss of appetite
   b. rising temperature
   c. halucinations
   d. restlessness

2. **Nancy Hedford was sent to Epsilon Canaris 3 to:**
   a. open up diplomatic relations
   b. meet Captain Kirk
   c. check its medical facilities
   d. prevent a war

3. **When Cochrane first encountered the Companion, he was:**
   a. dying
   b. exploring space
   c. 77 years old
   d. lonely

4. **When Scott attempts to backtrack the path of the shuttlecraft, he:**
   a. trails the traces of expelled oxygen
   b. checks for anti-matter residue
   c. retraces the craft's projected course
   d. follows the voice communications

5. **The Companion enters the Commissioner's body so that she can:**
   a. leave the planet
   b. know life as a human
   c. save the Commissioner from dying
   d. communicate with Cochrane